The Lasater Philosophy of Cattle Raising

by

LAURENCE M. LASATER

TEXAS WESTERN PRESS

THE UNIVERSITY OF TEXAS AT EL PASO

1972

DESIGN

Library of Congress Catalog Card No. 79-190505

ISBN 0-87404-037-X

PRINTED IN THE UNITED STATES OF AMERICA

FOR ANNETTE
and
OUR PARENTS

"South Africa's Dr. Jan C. Bonsma is said to have labeled the Lasater Beefmaster herd as near perfection in functional efficiency." [1]

Table of Contents

PHOTO BY MYRON WOOD

TOM LASATER

"It takes high hurdles to achieve high goals."

INTRODUCTION

TOM LASATER, founder of the BEEFMASTER breed, is one of those rare individuals who knew from childhood what profession he was going to pursue. He is fond of saying that ranching is his avocation as well as his vocation. It has been his life, his livelihood, and the basis of his philosophy for more than forty years now. During this period, he has successfully ranched in Texas and Colorado during times of continuous change. As his son and also as a rancher, I have seen his ideas emerge and, in many cases, be widely accepted. In the hope that the ideas he has expressed will be of interest to various readers and of special value to other ranchers, I have attempted to record some of his basic beliefs.

Tom Lasater's philosophy of cattle raising encompasses all aspects of the business from range ecology to merchandising. Perhaps his philosophy can be labeled "creative radicalism." He is unafraid to go against conventional theories; neither is he afraid to discard ideas and practices which he himself has used. He repeatedly has disproved and discredited traditional ideas long held by ranchmen, but only to offer a better concept to replace the discarded one — true constructive criticism, with the physician first healing himself. For example, I returned to the Lasater Ranch for two visits in 1970; both visits provided illustrations of my label of him as a "creative radical."

On the first visit in May, we were looking at the cow herd, and I noticed that the cows had lice. I asked my father how long since he had sprayed, and he said that he had stopped using all insecticides and was going to develop an insect-resistant herd. His theory is that the animal affected by parasites to the extent that it fails to perform will automatically eliminate itself. The Lasater Ranch no longer sprays and it has even eliminated chemically-treated backrubbers on the property. Feedlot cattle are not implanted with hormones, sprayed for flies, or given any other artificial assistance.

In the light of recent statements concerning ecology in general and insecticides in particular, this decision seems to have been logical and timely. Tom Lasater was perhaps alone at the time in his courage and foresight in subjecting his entire herd to the elimination of such practices, regardless of the immediate consequences.

During my second visit in September, I saw that the herd had survived the summer in fine shape without insecticides, and I predicted that this practice will spread in a few years, both for reasons of economy and health. At the same time, my father announced that he had stopped dehorning calves, beginning in 1970. After years of aspiring to have a perfectly dehorned herd, he had reached the conclusion that, since today's high-performance feeder cattle are slaughtered before they develop enough horn growth to make any difference, it was no longer feasible to dehorn, especially when one considered the labor situation. To dehorn in a humane manner and to do it correctly is a big job; for years this has been the biggest job of the year on the Lasater Ranch. Since I was a boy, dehorning had been so heavily emphasized and the dehorned cattle had received so many compliments from buyers that the idea of stopping the practice probably would never have occurred to me. Yet my father was perfectly willing to change his direction as soon as he saw that this long-standing practice was serving no purpose other than aesthetic.

Another example of innovative ideas is in Tom Lasater's use of advertising to merchandise. The Lasater Ranch has been a leader in the cattle industry in its use of advertising, having one of the oldest and best known campaigns in this country. The ranch advertises monthly in several trade journals at a substantial expense. The practice has obviously paid off, but the decision to start advertising was a far-sighted one and the results were not so obvious when my father began to advertise more than thirty years ago. His methods of advertising are unique in the industry in that the emphasis is on selling ideas rather than on selling cattle. The assumption is that a man who buys the philosophy will buy the cattle. The campaign is also unique in that each month it features a different picture of a LASATER BEEFMASTER in range condition.

My father is proud of the progress he has made in range and game management. He follows no fixed program, but in his own words, "I think Nature is smart as hell. I help as much as I can, but I try to let her do most of the work." This summarizes his basic approach to the cattle business. Ecology is "in" now, but it has been practiced for years on the Lasater Ranch. Tom Lasater's idea about wildlife is simply that, in addition to being beautiful, it also helps him to produce more beef. He allows no systematic hunting, trapping or poisoning of predators of any type, including coyotes and rattlesnakes. One day he and his foreman were talking in the pasture, and the foreman said, "Mr. Lasater, I shouldn't tell you this, but there's a rattlesnake right behind you." This prohibition of rattlesnake-killing has always been a source of irritation to his children and employees. Many years ago, in cooperation with a government program, prairie dogs were eradicated from the ranch, but my father has since regretted this and he imported some in order to restock the range.

As a result of these practices, Nature has found its balance and there are no longer excessive numbers of any one species, such as rabbits or coyotes as there were at other times. Abundant game exists and all concerned seem to be healthier as a result of these practices. The only creatures currently out of balance are the antelope and the Indians, and it may be necessary eventually to import some Indians to correct the situation. Otherwise, the only real change on the range is that BEEFMASTERS have taken the place of buffaloes.

The same basic ideas have been used in range management. No artificial seeding has been done nor have any poisonous plants been eradicated on the assumption that Nature will provide whatever is needed. My father recalled losing a heifer to locoweed in 1949, but has had no problems since that time. Each pasture is rested for a part of every year, with the movement of the cattle being dictated by a day-to-day observation of the condition of the range and the livestock. Tom Lasater has developed a unique pasture inventory, updated every fifteen days, which accurately reflects the stocking history of each pasture. The result of this program of cooperation with Nature has drawn world-wide acclaim from ranchers, ecologists, and other interested people.

The kernel of Tom Lasater's ideas about cattle raising is the concept of reproductive efficiency (not to be confused with "calving percentage," a term tossed about the coffee shops over the country). Since 1948, every cow that failed to wean a calf every year, beginning as a two-year-old, has been culled. This includes cows whose calves were killed by lightning, drowning, or by any other means. Dr. Jan Bonsma, who has probably done more than anyone else to popularize this concept of reproductive efficiency, has said that the simplest and most direct method of selecting for this trait is to follow this practice of ruthless culling, first adopted by the Lasater Ranch over twenty years ago. It is completely accurate and requires no particular skill, but only a great amount of courage and willpower. In talking about cattle with others, my father has found that oftentimes cattlemen claim, "we do it that way, too." In many cases, however, they are kidding themselves, for this philosophy of cattle raising (although it is based upon very simple principles) is actually practiced by very few ranchers.

Some people have said that BEEFMASTERS were begun thirty years too soon – meaning that if they were just now coming into being, they could enjoy the boom currently being experienced by the so-called "exotics." History proves, however, that thirty years is the time lapse between the creation of a revolutionary new concept and its acceptance by the cattle industry; therefore, the timing was probably right. The Lasater philosophy of cattle raising is summarized in Appendix B under the title "The Lasater Beefmaster Standard of Excellence."

Some time ago, my father received a telephone invitation from a banker to address a cattleman's gathering. He accepted with pleasure and asked why the banker was issuing the invitation. The banker replied that the ranchers in his area owed the bank about $14 million and that the ranchers had no idea how they would be able to pay it back. "Would you please come up and give them some ideas?" he asked.

My father's speech opened with the following comment: "Gentlemen, you are in a unique position in history. Almost anything you do will be better than what you are doing now." Even today, there is more truth than humor in this anecdote, for it describes the situation of cow-calf men everywhere. Perhaps many of them will recognize the relevance of the unique Lasater philosophy to cattlemen in all areas of the world, all of whom appear to be caught in a permanent cost-prize squeeze.

This book is based on the assumption that today's rancher wishes to continue ranching, and to do so he oftentimes must change his way of operating in order to stay in business. Perhaps some of the ideas advanced here will be relevant and applicable to those situations. In any event, it is "ideas" which are being sold here – not a particular breed of cattle. Concerning ideas, Tom Lasater has said, "Our minds, like parachutes, only function when open." Hopefully, the concepts presented here will be received with open minds and will also open minds. In some, perhaps my own interpretations have intruded. Others perhaps originated with my grandfather, Ed C. Lasater, who began ranching in South Texas at the turn of the century. But primarily they are all the thoughts embodied in one man – Tom Lasater – who "marches to the beat of a different drum."[2]

–Laurence M. Lasater
Múzquiz, Coahuila

PHOTO BY STEWARTS

"I would rather make a rancher out of a boy off the streets of New York or Tokyo than a boy raised on a conventional ranch." †

† All quotations followed by a dagger are by Tom Lasater.

CHAPTER I

THE ROLE OF MANAGEMENT

ONE OF THE GREATEST pleasures of being a cattleman is to visit a progressive ranch and to see how its owner or manager employs ingenuity to improve his operation. Traditionally, free interchange of ideas between ranchers has provided great benefits to those who partake of such discourse. None of the theories in this book will work in the absence of creative management. If useful, these ideas will have to be improved upon and adapted by the rancher to fit his individual needs. "Results are obtained by exploiting opportunities, not by solving problems."[3] To survive in today's circumstances, the ranch operator must, like any business executive, be concerned with improvement and innovation rather than with ordinary problem-solving.

A good manager is one who produces the maximum net income in a given situation while caring for his property. It is not possible to "save a profit" as the saying goes, but net income is greatly influenced by planning as well as budgeting and cost-control.

Many aspects are involved in planning; first and foremost is planning for production. This consists of ascertaining the productive capacity of a given operation and ensuring that this capacity is reached each year, regardless of circumstances. In the beginning stages, production-planning involves breeding sufficient females and then pregnancy-testing to ensure that the desired number of calves is on the way. If conception rate is low, additional bred females can be bought. Once an operation is established, a high level of reproductive efficiency will ensure maximum production each year.

Planning also involves the systematic maintenance of machinery and installations. Preventive maintenance is very important in ranching as it is in all businesses. For example, cup leathers on wells should be changed periodically before they wear out, and fences should be inspected frequently, especially in brushy areas.

Capital investments in improvements and equipment should be carefully planned with accurate records of cost and return on investment. All major purchases should be made on the basis of bids obtained well in advance of the actual purchase date. Cattle, as a rule, will not pay for lavish improvements or equipment, both of which must be kept simple, functional and durable. The only luxury permitted the rancher is that of having good cattle.

Effective budgeting and cost control, for both management and tax purposes, involves, first and foremost, an accurate, up-to-date set of double entry books. Depending on the size of the business, these books can be kept on a weekly or a monthly basis. These records should reflect only details needed to give the manager a fair picture of what is happening in his business. Either too much or too little detail is a bad thing. The accounts should quickly show what areas of the business are overly costly. Each year should begin with a projected budget for operations as well as projected sales. The ability to estimate accurately these figures is a key element in obtaining financing.

Many of the present concepts of range management are not adequate and are gradually being replaced. Historically, on the Great Plains, nature alternately deferred the land and ravished it with fire and enormous buffalo herds. The good manager works with nature while, at the same time, he pushes his land and cattle to the limit. In the final analysis, only the individual can decide what constitutes good husbandry in his situation. He must "Keep in mind that the ranchers who use rangelands are people who must ultimately apply ecological knowledge. Ecologists seldom operate ranches themselves."[4]

The achievement of maximum production on any property involves some system of pasture rotation. The manager of each cattle operation should coordinate his production plans with the type of land he has and the climate in his area, always with the aim of increasing productivity and improving his pastures. In extensive ranching operations such as those encountered in the Western United States, cross-fencing and drinking water are the keys to effective pasture usage and high levels of productivity. In more intensive stock-farming operations, improved farming and intensive pasture management techniques will play the decisive roles.

Vertical integration is here to stay and today's manager needs to know more about different aspects of the cattle business than did his predecessors. A good operator needs to acquaint himself with such areas as artificial insemination, cattle feeding, and meat merchandising. Each of these areas offers the individual manager ways to increase his net income; every rancher should give some thought to incorporating some, or all of these, into his operation.

Like all businesses, ranching is becoming increasingly complex. The rancher today, like any other executive, must be knowledgeable in his field. He must also be actively involved in the work done in his operation in order to be closely in touch with his land and cattle as well as with his employees. Always, a good ranch manager should cut needless expenses and practice good housekeeping. A neat, clean ranch is apt to be one that is well operated.

PHOTO BY DAROL DICKINSON

"The best fertilizer for any soil is the footprints of the owner."
CHINESE PROVERB

"The Breeder of animals directs the spark of life itself. The possibilities of his art are almost infinite." SOURCE UNKNOWN

CHAPTER II

A SOUND BREEDING PROGRAM

"A GOOD MANAGER must be in love with results."†

A sound breeding program, oriented toward results, should be based on the Five Commandments of Livestock Breeding.

The First Commandment is to select only for the SIX ESSENTIALS: *Disposition, Fertility, Weight, Conformation, Milk Production,* and *Hardiness.* Long range objectives must be clearly defined, drastically limited and ruthlessly executed. The immediate objective of any effective breeding program is to make each generation obsolete as quickly as possible.

The *six essentials* constitute the Standard of Excellence against which Tom Lasater evaluates his cattle. These are the keystones in his philosophy of cattle raising, and each the subject of a chapter in this book. The more objectives are limited, the faster they can be achieved.

The Second Commandment is to strive for reproductive efficiency. Until the calf is standing in the weaning pen, all else is academic. Reproductive efficiency consists of weaning a high percentage calf-crop while employing certain practices that tend to lower the percentage of calf crop weaned. These practices are (1) to keep 80% or more of each heifer crop and (2) to breed them at around 13-months-of-age for a short season of 65 days or less.

The Third Commandment is to performance test in a constant environment. Tom Lasater has often said, "Livestock should be bred, born, raised, performance tested and sold under the conditions in which they will produce." If there were a breeder of equal ability in every geographical area, there would be no need for long-distance movement of breeding stock.

The Fourth Commandment is to employ direct selection, which means selecting for the specific traits sought and not for a combina-

† All quotations followed by a dagger † are by Tom Lasater.

tion the breeder *hopes* will produce the desired results. If weight is desired, one should select for it by using scales and not by trying to "eyeball" the cattle. Rate of heritability is of little importance in a selection program. If fertility is desired, one must select for it regardless; by the same token, if a trait is not needed, don't select for it, regardless. In 1925, E. Parmelee Prentice was asked what the American dairy cow of the future would look like. He defined direct selection when he answered, "she will look like a cow that gives a hell of a lot of milk."

The Fifth Commandment is to utilize the adaptive powers of nature. Tom Lasater's policy is to ask the impossible of nature, and he often gets it. However, he recognizes that his "credit" with nature is limited; therefore, he limits his requests accordingly. For example, my father demands that his replacement heifers calve by twenty-four months of age and wean a heavy, long-age calf that year and each year thereafter. He does not also demand that these calves have a certain color haircoat or that they be possessed of other irrelevant characteristics.

There are various steps involved in establishing a sound breeding program based on the *six essentials*. The first is to select the breed best suited to the environment in which cattle are to be raised and a breed genetically able to produce the desired results in that environment. Six-hundred pound calves are not produced by a breed with a calf-crop average of four-hundred pounds.

The second step is to obtain the best genetic material the business can afford, either through the purchase of seedstock or through artificial insemination.

Thirdly, when a large enough and good enough gene pool has been created, close the herd and select for the *six essentials*. The mistake of closing the herd while better genes are available should not be made. Anyone not satisfied with the breeds now in existence can create his own breed by making a three-way cross of those which apparently offer the most for his environment and then by following Step Three. It has been firmly established that the three-way cross is the most potent combination available to the cattle producer. Since time is usually of the essence and there are many excellent herds of varied breeds available, any herd may be vastly upgraded in three generations, providing top sires or semen from same are used. Artificial insemination will greatly expedite the process.

The adoption of any permanent crossbreeding program is not recommended because of certain marked disadvantages. Some are very cumbersome from the management standpoint. Some crossbreeding programs necessitate always buying replacement stock with the recurrent expense, disease risk, dependence on another producer and problems of moving cattle and adapting them to a new environment each year. Any crossbreeding program limits the producer to a static herd, closing to him the profitable avenue of grading-up to a clearly-defined, reputable and valuable herd of cattle. An outcross is, however, indispensable in any existing herd whose rate of productivity in any essential characteristic, such as weaning weight, is below the rate available from another breed or line.

The cow-calf man should produce high-performance cattle and sell them effectively. To do this, he should select exclusively for beef-producing characteristics and retain ownership of his cattle at least through the feedlot. Cattle embodying the *six essentials* to a high degree will automatically be high-performing cattle at every stage. Heavy-weaning calves are efficient feeders. Long-bodied calves are heavy weaners. Long-bodied cattle yield a high percentage of primal retail cuts, and so on. "Form follows function."

Nature has correlated many desirable characteristics in beef cattle. A sound breeding program, based on the Five Commandments of Livestock Breeding, will take advantage of this correlation with the result that the cattle in question will improve rapidly in all areas, including many that the breeder had not planned. The basis for cattle breeding and range management is an understanding on the part of the rancher that he is laboring within a finely-tuned universe that functions better as he interferes less.

"When a bull or a cow needs a foot trim,
we let the packer trim them." †

CHAPTER III

DISPOSITION

TRADITIONALLY, disposition has probably received less consideration from cattlemen than any of the *six essentials*. It has always been important and today it is even more important because of increased labor costs.

An animal with a good disposition is one which is responsive and docile by nature and gentle by training. Many ranchers work their cattle with only family help, which serves as an acid test on *disposition*. Good cattle are beautiful animals and worthy of affection. The true cattleman instinctively dislikes mistreatment of his cattle, and realizes that mishandling is also poor business.

Two aspects are involved in obtaining some of the *six essentials:* selection and management. An operation that is deficient in either of these has no hope of having top cattle.

Selecting for disposition is simple. At weaning time, any difference in individuals is readily apparent in cattle raised under identical conditions. The bulk of animals with poor dispositions can be spotted at that time and culled. Thereafter, disposition is judged continually with any noticeably excitable or high-strung animals being periodically eliminated from the herd.

Various considerations are involved in managing for disposition. Obviously, no "cowboying" can be tolerated. There are very few situations on a well-managed ranch in the twentieth century where roping is justified for reasons other than for sport. Employees should not be allowed to carry ropes; thereby the temptation to rope is eliminated.

Well-designed pens and handling facilities help to keep cattle gentle. Every rancher has his own theories, but corrals and other such installations should be built with "cow-psychology" in mind. For example, few sets of pens in existence take into account the fact that cattle flow more smoothly from a long crowding pen (50-60 feet) into a long chute (50-60 feet) and then into the squeeze chute than from a short crowding pen and short chute. New feedlots have developed systems of handling cattle that are far superior to those encountered on the average ranch.

Supplementary feeding, which is an increasingly indispensable tool on well-managed ranches, is a great aid in gentling cattle and in checking them. Improved disposition is a benefit resulting from such feeding.

All replacement cattle should be gentled at weaning. This can be accomplished in four or five days, even if large numbers are involved. If the calves are not fed anything except pellets or grain for the first day or two, they will begin to get very hungry. They can then be placed in a smaller crowding pen and hand-fed hay, grain or pellets. Those that gentle down are turned back to the main pen on hay and grain. The more nervous individuals will gentle rapidly as they get hungrier. Those that refuse to submit to this type of handling should be culled.

The problem of "dark-cutter" beef is related to disposition. "Dark-cutter" beef is beef which exhibits a purplish-black to very black color. This condition does not affect the palatability of the meat, but the housewife will not buy it, for she thinks it must be old meat, which has a similar color.

The "dark-cutter" condition is related to stress and the production of adrenalin. The critical period in this condition is 12-24 hours after stress. Animals slaughtered during this time will be more apt to have this problem.[5]

Cattle are subject to stress in accordance with their genetic makeup. Wide variance exists between different herds of cattle. The breeder should recognize the importance of emotional stability in planning his program and, likewise, the feeder should take this into account in buying replacement cattle.

Any rancher can improve his cattle by selecting and managing for disposition. He will have better cattle and lower operating costs without any additional investment. The feeder, packer, and consumer will each benefit in turn from the breeder's decision to select for disposition. No one likes wild cattle, so why raise them?

"In culling every female that fails to wean a calf every year, regardless of reason, we lose some good ones but we get all the lemons." †

CHAPTER IV

FERTILITY

THE IMPORTANCE of fertility in the cattle business is obvious, and yet today's ranchmen have failed to produce cattle that are fertile, as we use the term here. Through his acute powers of observation over a long period of time, Dr. Jan Bonsma of South Africa has developed his own unique method of recognizing fertility, and has done much to awaken American cattlemen. Tom Lasater has reached the same goal through his method of culling any individual that does not wean a good calf every year, beginning as a two-year-old.

Periodically, interviews with leading cattlemen appear in the various trade journals. Something similar to the following exchange appeared recently in a well-known magazine:

Question: What percent calf crop do you get?
Answer: Over 95%.
Question: How long does it take you to get a 95% calf crop?
Answer: About eighteen months.

Percentage calf crop is the most abused, misunderstood and exaggerated statistic in the cattle industry. The cattleman in the interview cleverly said everything that could be said on the subject. It is a simple mathematical fact that cows bred more than 90 days do not calve every year.

Under the Lasater system, bulls go into service at 12½ to 14½ months of age. All age groups are bred under range conditions for a 65-day season beginning November 15th. Each cow or heifer must conceive under these conditions and then wean a good calf — no exceptions — or be culled.

Selection for reproductive efficiency consists of a short breeding season; males and females bred at 12½ to 14½ months and a calf from every cow every year — regardless. Reproductive efficiency also involves accomplishing the foregoing while keeping 80-90% of each heifer crop in order to intensify culling of the cow herd.

Heifers that do not calve before 25 months should be deducted from the calving percentage. After all, they are drys just like any cow who fails to produce. Often one hears a rancher claim that he does not need to pregnancy-test. The object of cattle raising (and the means of maximizing income from a given operation) is not to set one's goals so low that the cattle pass effortlessly, but rather to set them so high that only the best survive.

The female who fails to calve as a two-year-old can never catch her contemporary who does, as illustrated by the following chart:

Age of Cow in Days at Weaning Time	*Cow No. 1 Bred as Two-year-old Fails to Wean a Calf as Coming Seven*		*Cow No. 2 Bred as Yearling Calves Every Year*	
	*Total Wt. of Calves**	*Lbs. of Calf per day of age of cow*	*Total Wt. of Calves**	*Lbs. of Calf per day of age of cow*
1000 days (2 yrs. +)	—	—	550 lbs.	.55 lbs.
1365 days (3 yrs. +)	550 lbs.	.40 lbs.	1150 lbs.	.84 lbs.
2095 days (5 yrs. +)	1750 lbs.	.84 lbs.	2350 lbs.	1.12 lbs.
2825 days (7 yrs. +)	2350 lbs.	.83 lbs.	3550 lbs.	1.26 lbs.
3555 days (9 yrs. +)	3550 lbs.	1.00 lbs.	4750 lbs.	1.34 lbs.

**First calf weighs 550 lbs. — each succeeding calf weighs 600 lbs.*

As can be readily seen from the chart, Cow No. 2 produces 1200 pounds more beef than Cow No. 1. At thirty cents per pound, she generated $360 more income during her nearly ten years of production. Assume that Cow No. 2 weighs 100 pounds less at twenty cents per pound when she is sold and needs fifteen dollars of extra feed to breed as a yearling. Deduct $35 from $360, and Cow No. 2 still produced $325 more net income than Cow No. 1, or $32.50 per year additional profit.

Many ranchers claim that they would lose too many heifers or that their calves would be too poor if they adopted this drastic (but logical) system. In this case, two options exist:

1. Subject the cattle to the program just described, keeping only those that can and build a herd that meets this standard of reproductive efficiency.
2. Buy heifers that can perform.

Management plays an extremely important role in fertility. Once the foregoing principles are put into operation, any herd will become a fertile one within a short period of time, for all infertile females will be rapidly eliminated. Also cows that have difficulty calving or that do not take good care of their babies (thereby losing them) will be sold at weaning time.

Anybody can accomplish the foregoing if they have the nerve to stay with the program. The theory is very simple, but the practice is not. However, once this program is adopted, management becomes the key consideration in fertility.

The breeding season is the critical time of year on any ranch that subscribes to the foregoing. The cattle, both male and female, must be in thrifty condition to breed. They must be receiving everything they need from a nutritional standpoint. Energy, phosphorus, Vitamin A, and Iodine are among the critical elements most often lacking. Younger cattle should be separated from older cattle and special attention should be given to breeding in the pastures most favorable to a high conception rate.

Generally speaking, a ranch that breeds its cattle at approximately 13 months for a short season and demands a heavy, long-age calf every year, will adopt fall calving. There are two distinct breeding seasons: April 1st for spring calves and November 15th for fall calves. Breeding later than April 1st or later than November 15th will result in short-age calves at weaning. Some of the advantages of fall calving follow:

1. The critical period of any ranching operation is that encompassing the time from the beginning of the calving season to the end of the breeding season. Under the fall calving system, calves are weaned in the late spring or early summer. The cow herd rests during the summer months, and therefore, mends better and faster than it would have mended if rested during the winter months. The cows calve with ideal weather and grass conditions in the late summer and early fall, and due to these ideal conditions, are able to breed back more efficiently than cows calving and recuperating in the early spring months – which are the hardest months of the year.

2. Growthy heifers weaned in the late spring or early summer will mature sexually for breeding by November 15th; whereas the same

heifers weaned in November will have great difficulty developing through the winter for breeding April 1st under range conditions.

3. Under the same management, more calves can be produced on a given property under fall calving because of reproductive efficiency resulting from the advantages outlined in (1) and (2). The efficient production of calves is the business of the cattleman, and this is the principal reason for fall calving.

4. A secondary benefit of fall calving is selling all classes of feeder and slaughter cattle in the spring and summer when there are less cattle available for sale.

PHOTO BY FORREST BASSFORD

"Nature is smarter than all of us." †

"If I could breed a cow fifty feet long, I would." †

CHAPTER V

WEIGHT

THE VAST MAJORITY of cattle are marketed on a weighed basis. The importance of weight is universally recognized and yet the cattle industry, as a whole, has not achieved weaning weights that approximate those easily within its grasp.

Furthermore, cattlemen have only recently recognized the high degree of correlation that exists between weaning weight, fertility and feedlot performance, not to mention milk production. It has been said that by selecting for weaning weight alone, a man can improve his cattle in all aspects 70% as fast as all the most complex, computer-oriented management systems could hope to, by using nothing more complicated than a scale.

Under the present marketing system, the heavier weaning calves are docked as feeders, when actually they are the higher performers and should bring a premium.

In selecting males for weight under the Lasater system, two factors are involved: (1) weaning weight and (2) post-weaning gain. The weaning weight reflects the milking ability of the mother; the post-weaning gain indicates the individual's own capability.

At weaning time, the calves on the Lasater Ranch, all born within 65 days, are weighed in two groups, one for each month of the calving season. The calves are weighed on two consecutive days and these weights are averaged to determine the true weaning weight. The bull calves are compared with individuals with a maximum age differential of 30 days, all raised in the same pasture. These weights are considered relevant only to that year's calf crop on the Lasater Ranch and are not to be compared with other years or other ranches. The only function of the weaning weight is to compare the individual with his peers.

The post-weaning gain test is conducted under range conditions where most of the bulls will be used and, again, is only relevant to that particular group, all of whom are together during the test period. Under this unique system, before the animals are 12 months old, the breeder and his customers have all the information they need to evaluate these bulls, and the animals themselves are ready for light service. This method of testing is much less expensive than a feedlot gain test and does not render the animal unserviceable for use under range conditions, as is often the case with feedlot tests. Under today's system of gain-testing bulls, the tested cattle are too old, too fat and too expensive at the end of the test. Bulls need to be evaluated and in service by 13 months.

Selecting females for weight is a very simple process. At weaning time, lightweight heifers are culled. Thereafter, females are not culled on their own weight or appearance, but for raising a light or sorry calf.

Selecting cattle on the basis of actual weaning weight as opposed to adjusted weaning weight is one of the most valuable tools at the cattleman's disposal. Adjusted weaning weight tends to perpetuate the status-quo because low-producing cows often can slip by. The cattle industry has failed to use selection for weaning weight effectively with the result that cattle, in general, are not noticeably heavier than they were a few years ago. Few high-performance cattle are available to the feedlots, and most heifers are still not exposed to the bulls at thirteen months. Considering the current cost-price squeeze, it is imperative that ranchmen begin using *selection for weight* as a means of increasing their efficiency of production.

"Good genetics mean good economics." †

"In judging, we do not want to know the sire, or dam, as we might be influenced unduly" †

CHAPTER VI

CONFORMATION

IN SELECTING for conformation, what is really under consideration is carcass conformation. As Tom Lasater says, "the ideal conformation is exemplified by that animal whose carcass will yield the most pounds of tender, lean beef per pound of live weight." Fortunately, selection for this characteristic is not difficult because, given the chance, nature correlates many of the desirable traits in beef cattle such as body length, weaning weight, fertility, feedlot performance and cutability. Again, "form follows function."

Common sense must be exercised. Untold damage is done to different breeds by selecting for the wrong characteristics. The cattleman should not stipulate a certain body type or size in the hope that this will produce the desired results, but rather he should select individuals that are producing the desired results and let nature stipulate what body type or size is needed. Under this system, "bulls will look like bulls and cows will look like cows."†

To evaluate cattle by visual means without reference to other information is nearly impossible. This is the basic fallacy underlying the show ring and it is one of the reasons the Lasater Ranch does not show cattle. Most judging of cattle, both in the show ring and out, is done solely by visual means, without reference to background information. In addition, "honest" cattle, in working condition, cannot show favorably in a show ring situation; thereby the fitting of cattle for showing results in concurrent perversion of real values. Showing and selling cattle under artificial conditions is one of the great handicaps to genetic improvement in our cattle today.

Our concept of the ideal conformation is improving rapidly. Any experienced cattleman can "yield-grade" his own cattle by culling individuals that are weak in the hindquarters or show tendencies toward being "wasty" cattle, giving carcasses with undesirable fatty deposits. These fatty deposits tend to show clearly in the following areas: the brisket, the flank and the top-line. Short-coupled, deep-bodied, flat-backed cattle are "wasty." Since 85% of the retail value of the carcass is represented in the round, loin, rib and chuck, a person judging beef cattle on conformation should concentrate on the area from the hindquarters to the heart-girth and ignore the forequarter and head.

Structural soundness is an aspect of conformation that can be judged on the hoof. A defect that could impair the individual's ability to perform (such as bad legs, pendulous sheath or weak eyes) should result in that individual's being culled. Each breed has weaknesses characteristic of it, and devotees of all types of cattle should work diligently to eliminate these weaknesses through selection.

PHOTO BY DAROL DICKINSON

"Type on the hook, not type on the hoof." †

CHAPTER VII

HARDINESS

"HARDINESS IS EXEMPLIFIED by those individuals which carry on their relentless production assignment year after year with minimum assistance," according to Tom Lasater.

Every environment tests cattle in some fashion whether it is the cold, heat, drought, too much rain, parasites, rough terrain, predators, low quality feed or any other of the many problems that affect the rancher.

Cattle should be raised in the environment in which they are to be used. Given that prerequisite, they should be able to adapt to the particular disadvantages of their geographic location. If they do not, obviously they will be unable to breed at 13 months or to wean a heavy, long-age calf nine months old or older every year.

The hardy animal must perform with only the minimum amount of help. It is out of the question, for example, to trim bulls' hooves or to milk cows with udder troubles. Individuals such as these should be culled in order to eliminate such uneconomical defects from the herd.

Very little attention has been given to selection for hardiness by the cattle industry. More emphasis has been placed on medication than on breeding trouble-free cattle with the result that, to some extent, United States producers have bred the vigor out of their cattle. This partly accounts for the fact that so many feedlot cattle are bothered by stress and respiratory illnesses. Mexican feeder cattle command a premium in the United States because they come from a harsh environment and have not been pampered; as a result the buyer experiences little difficulty with sickness and death loss.

The health and disease prevention program adopted on a ranch should be carefully planned with a view toward vaccinating only for diseases such as Blackleg and others that must be prevented. The practice of widespread vaccination for Septicemia, for example, has probably contributed greatly to the lack of resistance that today's cattle have for this disease. The Lasater Ranch vaccinates only for Blackleg and Malignant Edema at birth and again at weaning, and heifer calves are officially vaccinated for Brucellosis. Cattle have been shipped to various points in the Western Hemisphere, traveling for as long as two weeks without any serious stress problems.

PHOTO BY DAROL DICKINSON

"Meet a real Mom."†

CHAPTER VIII

MILK PRODUCTION

THE 1971 DROUGHT brought sharply into focus the idea of weaning calves early to "save" their mothers. Creep feeding has no place in a normal year, and, even in a bad year, the burden of raising a decent calf should be left to the cow, even if it involves supplementing her. Our cheapest gains are produced from birth to weaning.

Selection for milk production is a simple matter of evaluating the cow's milking abilities as reflected in her calf's weaning weight. In the case of bulls, herd sires are selected from bulls with top weaning weights thereby perpetuating the blood from heavy-milking females. Heifers are culled on weight at weaning; cows weaning light-weight calves are also eliminated.

During the years in which this policy has been observed, nature has produced remarkable udders on the Lasater Ranch cows; the udders resemble those of milking types, but are not pendulous and do not have large, irregular teats. Instead, they are compact and trim, yet with great capacity.

"The degree to which performance testing is used as a gimmick, to this same degree, its true purpose is being defeated." †

CHAPTER IX

BULL POWER

CATTLEMEN often say that bulls are half the herd. This underestimates the importance of the sires used, for "any bull battery will remake a cow herd in its own likeness in three generations."† An investment in bulls, combined with the management and selection practice outlined, is the most economical means of upgrading cattle. Grading-up, however, is much slower than buying both top males and females.

The first step in purchasing seed stock is to locate a reliable breeder that is raising and performance-testing cattle under conditions comparable to or harsher than the environment in which the animals are to be used. Tom Lasater has expressed it:

> "Take a burro that has been raised on broken glass and tin cans and start feeding him oats and he will go to town. But take a burro that has been raised on oats and demote him to tin cans and broken glass and he won't do so well. We can go upstairs but we can't go back down, nutritionally speaking."

The current popularity of the "exotics" is a case in point. All these breeds are British Isles or European farm-raised cattle. To think that these animals can significantly increase hardiness and milk production in the United States range cattle is a fallacy. It is unlikely that any combination of European breeds can equal the combination of Brahman with European blood in overall mothering ability under range conditions in North or South America.

It is rumored that one of the new imported breeds currently enjoying tremendous vogue in the United States has serious eye troubles. An American rancher on a visit to the new breed's country of origin asked a native what he did about pinkeye. The native replied that this presented no problem, for afflicted animals were left in the house, out of the sun for several days; this always cleared up the problem. The difficulties encountered in moving cattle to radically different environments cannot be overestimated.

The influence of the "exotics," however, combined with Dr. Bonsma's teaching has created a healthy concern with genetics and broadened the use of artificial insemination.

It is unreasonable to expect cattle raised on a small stockfarm to prosper in a big desert country, for example, and yet this has, in effect, been standard operating procedure in the cattle business. Cattle raised in hard country, on the other hand, will adapt to stockfarm conditions. The failure to recognize the importance of the background of breeding stock has been, and is, a basic problem in the cattle industry.

The third consideration in buying breeding stock is merchandising, which includes performance-testing. The present methods are not adequate to the needs of the day. In the case of performance-testing, Tom Lasater has the following to say: "For a breeder to be true to himself and attain his objectives, he must refrain from changing practical environmental and management practices for the purpose of enabling his cattle to look better on a performance test."

The purpose of performance-testing is evaluation, not selling. That high-performing cattle should sell better is only a by-product of a valid program. An animal that has been excessively pampered will be unable to perform its task, thereby defeating the original purpose of performance-testing, which is identification of those individuals that are profitable.

The methods of merchandising all classes of cattle today need to be completely changed. Some proposed changes in the marketing of slaughter follow in Chapters XI and XII. In the case of seed stock, three aspects of merchandising need to be considered: (1) age (2) sales (3) price.

Bulls sold for breeding purposes should be delivered at 13 months or younger, sexually mature and ready for light service. This allows time for the producer and buyer to evaluate them in terms of weaning weight and post-weaning performance. The buyer can begin to get some return on his investment immediately and, more importantly, to adapt the bulls to his environment. At thirteen months or younger, profit to the producer is at its maximum and cost to the buyer is at its minimum.

Another important consideration in buying bulls is disease risk. Venereal disease in cattle is recognized as an increasingly widespread problem. The risk in buying replacement stock can be considerably reduced by purchasing only young, virgin bulls.

Locating a reliable breeder is basic to the success of any cattle program. The breeder should have a well-managed, clearly-defined program of selection, based on the *six essentials,* and should be willing to explain his merchandising system in detail. The intrinsic value of seedstock is a reflection of the character of the breeder. After making this survey of the man and his operation, the buyer should be able to conclude whether or not the herd in question is free of disease or other problems.

Females can be sold as open heifers, as bred cows, or as pairs; the decision depends strictly on what is best for buyer and seller in each instance.

The present selling techniques often distort intrinsic values and the decision-making process. All selling of seed stock should be based on the real value of the animal, determined through careful evaluation by both buyer and seller. Advance contracting with all relevant conditions specified is the only selling technique that is viable from a long-range standpoint.

The Lasater Ranch has pioneered the merchandising of breeding cattle through its contracts sent out far in advance. The order of selection, in this instance, is determined by a drawing which includes all contracts returned within fifteen days. Price, in turn, is determined by order of selection with the buyers using the necessary performance data to evaluate the cattle themselves. This system is absolutely fair as the first buyer pays more than the second and each knows what the other is paying. The only problem presently being encountered with this system is not having enough bulls to satisfy the demand – which is a nice problem to have.

Some other ranchers are using similar methods effectively. F. R. Carpenter of Hayden, Colorado, prices his bulls based on rate-of-gain with selection made just before weaning. Dr. Watt Casey of Albany, Texas, contracts his bulls on a first-come, first-served basis with order of selection determining price. The buyer has access to complete performance records. Dr. Casey has had long-time success with selling bulls on a sliding scale of prices.

The problem with the methods of selling currently in vogue is that sound decision-making is not possible in the circus atmosphere of the sales ring where buyers are motivated more by the prevalent mood and by the strength of bidding than by hard facts. It is unfortunate, but true, that many cattlemen do not have confidence in their ability to judge cattle and would rather have deceptively incomplete information and other bidders help them. It is easier to pay a thousand dollars for a bull on which someone else bid $975 than it is to walk into a pen of a hundred bulls to top one out with the same crowd looking on.

In general, cattle in their working clothes do not fit in the setting and atmosphere of the sales barn. "Fat covers a multitude of sins," or "fat may cover a multitude of virtues."†

The third consideration in the overall merchandising of seed stock is price. Possibly the most dangerous thing that can happen to a breed of cattle is for it to become overly popular. "The man hasn't been born who will cull high-priced cattle."† The so-called purebred operator has one reason for existing, and that is to produce seed stock to be used in the production of slaughter cattle. Any purebred man whose top-selling bulls are too expensive for a progressive, commercial operator is pricing himself out of the market.

Inflated prices, with the resultant slowdown in culling, have ruined many breeds of cattle and some of the breeds most popular today, which are undoubtedly fine cattle, are being ruined by the people that are promoting them for their own short-term financial gain. The following is a partial list of practices that are common throughout the industry and detrimental to the breed and breeder involved:

1. Removing a cancer-eye and continuing to use the animal.

2. Operating on an infected or pendulous sheath and keeping the bull or selling him for breeding.

3. Failing to slaughter a cow who has had a caeserian delivery or a prolapsed uterus.

4. Attempting to hand breed a female of low fertility which has

failed to pasture-breed in the time allotted to other females on the ranch.

5. Not slaughtering any animal with foot, leg or udder problems or any other structural problems whatsoever.

Artificial insemination is potentially a very valuable tool and a benefit both to the purebred man and the commercial producer. The sale of semen is a potential bonanza that exists for those who produce the most promising seed stock. This semen should be priced in accordance with the principles just elaborated. Such is not the case in many instances today. For the man producing slaughter cattle, access to semen from whatever bulls he chooses means that his horizons are limited only by the validity of his choice and the effort he is willing to make.

The Lasater Ranch has used multiple-sire herds exclusively for many years in the belief that only nature can make the correct choice as to which bull actually settles a cow in heat. There are many factors, such as personality and semen viability, which no one is presently qualified to evaluate. The use of single-sire herds can result in favoring individuals whose practical fertility may be low.

Following this same line of reasoning, when artificial insemination is employed, Tom Lasater advocates using four or five bulls in rotation, or preferably, using mixed semen which results in a situation similar to natural service in a multi-sire herd where a cow may be covered by several different bulls. The mixed semen idea is still in the theoretical stage.

One of the principal advantages of a multiple-sire herd combined with a short breeding season is that all cows have the opportunity to conceive in the first heat period. Also, individuals within a closed herd become increasingly similar due to their sharing a common gene pool.

Obviously, the commercial operator who finds the source he needs for seed stock in accordance with the ideas expressed here and then hesitates to pay a decent price for those animals will quickly be eliminated from the business, unless he has other means by which to sustain himself.

"A good cow is a cow that weans a good calf every year. Period." †

CHAPTER X

COW POWER

THE MOST SERIOUS management error in the ranching industry is the slaughter of high percentages of each heifer crop. The Lasater Ranch, after forty years of intensive management and selection, keeps 80-90% of its heifer calves and culls 20-30% of its breeding-age females each year. This rapid turnover or "turning the genetic crank" is the basis for the dramatic improvement evident in their herd each year. This improvement in the cow herd is the most profitable aspect of the cow-calf business. Properly considered, feeder steers or bulls are a by-product of a ranching operation, not its principal one, as the matter is traditionally viewed.

What are the reasons for selling heifers? The most common reason offered is that the rancher does not have room for a high percentage of his heifer crop as replacements. This generally means that he is not breeding his heifers at thirteen months or not doing any significant culling on his cow herd. Breeding young and culling rigorously are practices indispensable to the success of any cattle operation. The problem in an intensive selection process is not having enough replacements to cull all the cows that should be culled

A rancher who still does not feel that he has room for most of his heifers should try breeding for twenty-one days only. Not to recognize the necessity of keeping heifers is not to recognize the infinite possibilities for improvement open to the producer. For a rancher to say that he does not have room for many heifers is the same as saying that he has too much money.

The second reason commonly encountered for not saving heifers is that the heifers are not good enough. If the heifer crop is not better than their mothers, it simply means that the bulls in use are not up to standard, and this situation should be remedied immediately.

Viewed from a strictly economic standpoint, the sale for eventual slaughter of weanling heifers is not feasible for two reasons. First and foremost, a cull cow is always worth more than a heifer for commercial purposes. The gross sales of any ranching operation will be dramatically increased by culling cows instead of heifers. Secondly, it is obviously not sensible to invest in really good bulls if all their progeny are going to be slaughtered. The idea is to obtain the best genetic material one can afford and profit from this by keeping large numbers of heifers and exposing them to the best breeding available.

These ideas should be commonplace. The fact that they are not makes them the most important in this book. The following steps apply anywhere in any set of circumstances:

1. Buy the best bulls available as defined in Chapter IX. If possible, buy females from the same source.

2. Breed all females on the same day every year for a short season. Twenty-one days should be everyone's goal. Heifers are bred at approximately 13 months. Breeding early puts pressure on sexual maturity.

3. Pregnancy-test after the breeding season and sell open heifers. Open cows can be sold at weaning time.

4. Cull all females that fail to wean a calf for any reason whatsoever.

5. Cull the cows weaning the worst calves in accordance with replacements available. A light calf costs just as much to produce as a heavy one.

6. Cows should nurse an average of at least 9½ months. "A cow, like a tractor, must work most of the time."†

7. Keep 80-90% of weanling heifers as replacements.

This program is called "population genetics" and involves mass selection for clearly defined principles combined with rapid turnover in both males and females. It is sad, but true, that the traditional cattleman concentrates his selection efforts on his heifers, based in many instances on evaluating the heifer's head as she comes down the chute.

Another time-honored practice is that of calving-out cull cows that happen to be bred back. It would seem far more logical and profitable to ship these females at weaning time and replace them with heifers.

In addition to fertility, a cow herd must have longevity and size. "The salvage value of the cow when sold represents a major portion, if not all, of the profit on that cow. Hence, that salvage value must be high through weight."†

Never cull simply on age. The cow of advanced age whose calves are still meeting all production standards is the gem for which everyone is looking. She is introducing effective longevity into the herd. Older cows are more efficient beef producers than younger cows.

Production efficiency and selection efficiency are greatly affected by longevity. Net longevity can be calculated by deducting the number of non-productive years as a heifer from the average age at which cows in a given herd become sub-fertile or infirm. The greater the net longevity, the fewer heifers are needed to replace old cows and the more heifers can be used to replace low-producing cows. Therefore, assuming equal calving percentages, if Herd A has greater net longevity than Herd B, it will improve more rapidly.[6]

These principles are simple. Putting them into effect is not, which accounts, in part, for the fact that they are not generally followed. If one subscribes to the ideas expressed thus far it becomes obvious that heifer management is a key consideration in any ranching operation.

As has been stated before, fall calving is probably the only means of achieving these goals. The Lasater Ranch calves for 65 days beginning in mid August and weans at about nine-months-of-age. The cows are in excellent shape at calving time, and are grazing range in peak condition after calving and again before weaning. Under this system, they are weaning long-age, very heavy calves.

The heifer calves are thoroughly gentled at weaning time and the bottom end of the crop goes to the feedlot. The rest are summered on excellent grass and are ready to breed November 15th without receiving supplemental feed. Many ranch operations require feeding from weaning until breeding because they do not have either the quality of heifers or grass conditions encountered in this instance.

These thirteen-month-old females are bred to bulls of the same age at a ratio of 1:10 for 65 days starting November 15th, at the beginning of the Colorado Plains winter. They are pregnancy-tested and only those that are bred stay in the Lasater herd. This is the first major selection that is done on these heifers. In this manner, all females that are not highly fertile in a practical sense are eliminated forever. As has been said before, "we lose some good ones, but we get all the lemons."†

Not only are all undesirables quickly identified and disposed of under this system, but those that stay are on schedule for life. Getting heifers bred at an early age and during a short season determines the entire course of their reproductive lives. It is thereby assured that every one of them will be profitable every day of her life because the minute she fails to wean a calf, and a good one, she immediately delivers herself as a dividend. In other words, on the Lasater Ranch, every female two years and older produces a dividend every year. If the year begins with 600 females 24 months old or older, there are 600 cash dividends that year.

A cow's only reason for being is to produce calves, and, logically enough, they should be evaluated only on the basis of the weight and quality of their calves. One of the tragedies of the ranching business is that cattlemen cull cows on their appearance when the cows doing most for their offspring will be doing so at the expense of their own appearances.

From the ideas presented here, it is obvious that record keeping in the conventional sense is a waste of time and serves only to obscure the important considerations. Tom Lasater sums it up as follows: "Keeping records doesn't require a file case full of papers. All we have on our cows is a year brand, and we know that if the cow hasn't produced and weaned a good calf every year, she wouldn't be there at all."

The cattleman traditionally prides himself on selection and management of his females, and yet this has been his greatest failing. Over the years he has butchered the very animals that could have helped him out of the desperate straits in which he now finds himself. The following from a well-known trade journal seems appropriate.

Incredible as it may seem, a lot of livestock breeders have come to the conclusion that they've been going backward for the past 50 years. Among those candid enough to admit this bitter conviction are directors of the Hampshire Sheep Association. At their recent meeting in Portland, they looked over a picture of the top pen of ewe lambs at the 1919 Chicago International; then, comparing those lambs with subsequent and current winners, several of the directors said they'd like to start all over with lambs like the 1919 winners.

"One would get the idea that the last 50 years in breeding has been lost. What you observe here can be applied to other breeds and to other species of livestock as well," says a soul-searching news release from association headquarters.

Many breeders have been inclined to blame the college professors for picking the wrong type in the show ring. Perhaps some of our shows have been misleading. We allowed ourselves to be led astray by looks and show tactics. We, as breeders, failed to follow the true purpose of any breed – utility. Appearance meant more to us than efficiency of production of the quality of the product to be consumed. . . .[7]

Females are the basic business of the livestock breeder, which is a fact that many have failed to recognize. The cattleman has often culled heifers instead of cows and evaluated cows on their appearance rather than the value of their calves. A cow's only purpose is to produce calves, and that is the only yardstick by which she should be evaluated.

PHOTO BY THE LASATER RANCH

"Truth is beautiful and profitable." †

"Hide color doesn't matter when the T-Bone is on the platter."
MARY CASEY LASATER

Incredible as it may seem, a lot of livestock breeders have come to the conclusion that they've been going backward for the past 50 years. Among those candid enough to admit this bitter conviction are directors of the Hampshire Sheep Association. At their recent meeting in Portland, they looked over a picture of the top pen of ewe lambs at the 1919 Chicago International; then, comparing those lambs with subsequent and current winners, several of the directors said they'd like to start all over with lambs like the 1919 winners.

"One would get the idea that the last 50 years in breeding has been lost. What you observe here can be applied to other breeds and to other species of livestock as well," says a soul-searching news release from association headquarters.

Many breeders have been inclined to blame the college professors for picking the wrong type in the show ring. Perhaps some of our shows have been misleading. We allowed ourselves to be led astray by looks and show tactics. We, as breeders, failed to follow the true purpose of any breed — utility. Appearance meant more to us than efficiency of production of the quality of the product to be consumed. . . . [7]

Females are the basic business of the livestock breeder, which is a fact that many have failed to recognize. The cattleman has often culled heifers instead of cows and evaluated cows on their appearance rather than the value of their calves. A cow's only purpose is to produce calves, and that is the only yardstick by which she should be evaluated.

"Truth is beautiful and profitable." †

PHOTO BY DEITS

"Hide color doesn't matter when the T-Bone is on the platter."
MARY CASEY LASATER

CHAPTER XI

THE FEEDLOT INDUSTRY

THE FEEDLOT INDUSTRY is beset by the problems facing all business; tight money, high interest, high feed costs, expensive replacement cattle and fed cattle selling on a depressed market. This segment of the cattle trade is also being hurt by problems of its own devising, principal among them being: feeding the wrong kind of cattle, ineffective merchandising and glamour. The principal considerations in the profitability of feeder cattle are daily gain and margin which are directly related to the capabilities of the animal involved and merchandising techniques.

As already stated, feedlot performance is directly correlated with weaning weight. As a rule, heavy-weaning calves will be high-performers in the feedlot. Incredible as it may seem, today's cattle trade discriminates against these cattle, price-wise. The ideal feeder animal is a heavy weaning-age calf, either a crossbred or from a herd selected for the *six essentials,* that has been preconditoned at the ranch and is ready to go on full feed. The weight depends on the background of the cattle, but the heavier the better, without creep feeding.

These heavy, high-performing calves can be weaned directly into the feedlot and finished on a high-concentrate ration before one-year-of-age, thereby eliminating the "stocker" and "growing-ration" phase. The pasture and roughage made available through this change could be fed to brood cows.

Cattle should be fed for "eatability" only, or in other words, they should be in the feedlot for much shorter periods of time. This would have two beneficial results. First, today's average 600-pound carcass contains 125-150 pounds of fat, which the consumer does not want. The new type of cattle, combined with a shorter feeding period, would substantially reduce this wasteful situation.

Secondly, grain needed for human consumption could be diverted from the feedlot industry. Few countries can afford the luxury of feeding as much grain to livestock as is fed in America, and it would probably be better business for Americans to sell more grain for export rather than feeding it.

In other words, the cattle industry has within its grasp the means of running substantially greater numbers of brood cows, weaning heavier calves and doing so with less grain consumption. This saving in grain purchased is net profit to the producer segment of the industry.

The cattle industry has never distinguished between "held-back" cattle and high-performing ones. The former will always be profitable to the buyer, if they are available. However, they represent no profit for the producer and it is to be hoped that very little of the pen space now available will be filled with this type of feeder cattle in years to come.

Replacement cattle with the bred-in capability to gain over 3.5 pounds per day would assure a profit to the producer and the feeder provided they are effectively merchandised. The present system of selling slaughter cattle needs to be completely changed by those presently producing beef in order to give them their share in the beef dollar. Tom Lasater's proposals in this regard are the subject of Chapter XII. In addition, the feedlot industry should take the lead in advocating a complete overhaul of the government grading system. The present method of grading does not reflect the dollar value of a carcass, as clearly illustrated by the following:

On the basis of cutting tests involving hundreds of beef carcasses, the Livestock Division found that similar weight choice grade carcasses vary as much as 15 percent in the yield of trimmed boneless cuts from the round, loin, rib and chuck. These major cuts represent about 85 percent of the retail value of the carcass, but may frequently account for less than half the carcass weight.

At prevailing prices for 1,000-pound choice grade slaughter steers or 600-pound choice grade carcasses, a 15 percent variation in yield means a retail value difference of more than $100.00 per carcass. While this much variation is the exception rather than the rule, differences of $25 to $30 are not uncommon. The magnitude of the extremes is important, however, because it indicates the wide latitude for selection and improvement.[8]

The cattle business must learn to differentiate between dressing percentage and cutability. High-performing cattle that are high in cutability should be identified early in the process and cattle feeders should pay a premium for them, thereby encouraging an increase in production of this type of animal. Again, the cattle industry is plagued by buying and selling on averages.

For the good of everyone in the business, the feeding of young bulls should become standard procedure. It is generally conceded that feeding young bulls instead of steers would make the cattle industry 10% more efficient in the production of beef from males. Bulls gain faster and more efficiently than steers; they yield a higher percentage of trimmed retail cuts and no difference exists in the quality of the meat when slaughtered at young ages. In Texas alone, this overall saving would be equivalent to producing an additional 127,000 head of 1,000-pound fed cattle.

Glamour is the enemy of all sound business practice. The feedlot industry has been hurt by having passed through a very glamorous epoch. It is very probable that many of the elaborate installations encountered are more effective in attracting customers than in feeding cattle.[9] Naturally, in hard times investments of this sort become a liability. Various periods of excessive profits greatly fanned the flames of expansion and many feedlots were built because of the availability of money rather than the availability of management.

Having dwelt at some length on what is wrong with the feedlot industry, it is only fair that its many important accomplishments be pointed out. Tremendous strides have been made in cattle handling, nutrition and health. The recent feedlot boom has introduced the cattle industry to a level of sophistication in finance heretofore undreamed of. From all appearances, the feedlots will be one of the first major businesses to solve its own pollution problem. The feedlot industry is tremendously exciting, and everything it has accomplished is for the good of the entire cattle trade.

"Every industry in America has the capacity to produce a surplus, but they seldom do so because they have developed a successful marketing technique, including supply management. For 37 years we have been dosing ourselves with the wrong medicine."

CHARLES B. SCHUMAN
Past President-American Farm Bureau

CHAPTER XII

ACS—PRONOUNCED "AX"

THE BEEF PRODUCER should work toward getting a bigger percentage of the beef dollar, rather than getting more for his product. With the onslaught of substitutes, synthetics and imports, he will be fortunate to maintain price levels already achieved. "Is it an inherent, immutable characteristic of the livestock producer that he must suffer disastrous, unpredictable fluctuations in the market for his product, even though retail meat prices remain perfectly stable at high levels?"[10] It is to no avail to supply the market with a more desirable animal if the producer is not fairly reimbursed for his efforts.

The cattleman should take as his goal the production of acceptable quality at minimum price. He should concentrate on lowering costs and producing good, lean beef, leaving to specialists the production of cattle for the "gourmet" market. He should also leave public relations work to the segments of the industry closer to the consumer. The housewife likes beef, but she is no more interested in the problems of producing it than is the rancher in the problems Ford Motor Company encounters in manufacturing his pickup.

As Ralph Nader very aptly said in a recent speech, "the big fallacy of reform is that it's going to succeed. What really provides stamina for this kind of work is the knowledge that you will never succeed, that basically all you're trying to do is to reduce our problems to the level of tolerability."

Two steps must be taken to reduce the economic problems of the beef producer to the level of tolerability. Neither require a major capital investment on the part of the producer. They are: (1) Abandonment of the present grading system in favor of one which fairly reflects leanness, tenderness and flavor; (2) Organization of beef producers.

One group of prominent cattlemen, Better Beef, Inc., is giving of its time, money and effort to provide a rallying point for the reform of today's system of merchandising beef cattle. F. R. Carpenter, President of Better Beef, Inc., gave an address entitled "The Case for the Cattle Producer" at the organization's first annual convention in Denver. In it he clearly stated the case for reform of today's marketing system.

Carpenter began by saying that a new product called "fed beef" has revolutionized all phases of the cattle business by changing consumer preference and increasing per capita consumption from 59 pounds in 1950 to 114 pounds in 1970. He went on to say that the cow-calf producer is the "forgotten man" in sharing the prosperity of this expansion, and that the reason for this is not sloth or inefficiency, but frozen cattle prices, directly traceable to antiquated marketing practices by the packers.

Carpenter added that the hanging beef carcass has always been the standard of value of cattle for slaughter, whereas the actual value of the retail cuts in each carcass should determine what the producer is paid. Until this fiction is abolished, it will not be possible for those producing higher-cutting cattle to be paid for their efforts. He closed by saying that the producers themselves will have to reform this market monstrosity. Mr. Carpenter's speech is reprinted in Appendix A.

The present beef grading system reflects neither the "eatability" nor the true dollar value of a carcass. The new system should tell all interested parties from producer to consumer what they are entitled to know about a cut of meat. Those producing more efficient cattle should be recompensed for their efforts. No breed should be discriminated against and young bulls should be able to grade. Under the present grading system, it is difficult, if not impossible, for a Holstein to grade choice. There is no corollary indication that Holsteins are not efficient producers of high-quality eating meat.

Organization is the second way in which the cattleman can increase his share of the beef dollar, and should accompany reform of the present grading system. Following are Tom Lasater's recommendations for obtaining effective bargaining power for the cattle industry. He proposes calling the organization American Cattle Sales — abbreviated ACS and pronounced ax.

1. Cattle will be sold for slaughter only. Selling service to be available to all stockholding members who sell beef or dairy cattle for slaughter within the United States.

   a. All slaughter sales will be made on a grade and yield basis.

   b. A new grading system is to be devised which will accurately reflect Tenderness, Flavor and Muscle Yield without regard to age, breed or sex.

2. All policy decisions shall be made by a national board of directors, composed of one elected director from each state board.

   a. Each state board of directors will be composed of one representative from each county, elected by the stockholders from that county.

   b. The duties of each state board shall be advisory.

3. ACS will begin accepting slaughter cattle for sale only when the corporation controls more than a prescribed minimum percentage of the total slaughter cattle nationally, as well as more than a prescribed percentage of the total slaughter cattle within each state which is ready to participate.

   a. Each member will contract to sell all of his slaughter cattle through ACS perpetually. If he wishes to withdraw, he must give ACS at least one year's advance notice in writing.

   b. At the time of a given sale, the stockholder will receive only a specified percentage of the net value of his cattle. Final payment will be on a quarterly basis. Final net price per pound to be received by a member will be the average net price per pound received for all cattle of the equivalent grade and yield which were sold during that quarter. The seller will be paid interest on the unpaid balance on his account from date of sale to settlement.

4. At such time as the national board may determine, sales quotas may be based upon average sales for some previous period of time. Thus, production can be encouraged or discouraged as market potential dictates.

Ideally, one of the already existing cattlemen's organizations should adopt these proposals. Better Beef, Inc. could provide those interested with the leadership necessary to reform the industry.

Those interested should write to Better Beef, Inc., Box 40, Hayden, Colorado, 81639.

Since cattle of all breeds or combinations of breeds received by ACS will be evaluated on the same basis, ACS stockholders will be motivated to produce cattle of maximum value under the revised grading system. This new grading system will reflect a beef cattle standard of excellence that concerns itself solely with beef-making characteristics.

ACS is envisioned as a profitable organization, operating as a gigantic commission firm, selling only stockholder's cattle. Cattle to be slaughtered off grass would be handled on a straight commission basis. Feedlot cattle would be custom fed for the rancher in feedlots belonging to ACS or on contract with existing custom feedlots. Regardless, the producer would receive full benefit from an "economy of scale" since the organization would be handling large quantities of livestock and feeds at a given time. In addition, beef futures could be effectively used to stabilize the market.

Other benefits would result from this cattlemen's union. It would be financially able to hire the very best personnel in all related fields; for example, feedlot nutrition, finance and merchandising of fed beef. ACS could expand into hauling and processing beef as well as export. The cattle industry could also use this organization as a means of planning and financing adequate, meaningful research. The horizons are absolutely limitless.

The means are at hand for the beef raisers to produce more and get more for it with little or no capital investment. It will be interesting to see whether or not today's cattlemen have the initiative and the good sense to begin doing business on a businesslike basis, as most other segments of the industry were forced to do long ago and as other industries have done for even longer.

"They're better when they hurry." †

Suspension fences and suspension gates — solutions to the perennial problem of cost and function. In this instance, line posts of 2" pipe are 100 feet apart with the twisted steel stay every 20 feet.

CHAPTER XIII

SUSPENSION FENCES AND SUSPENSION GATES

Suspension fences were pioneered by Tom Lasater and have met with worldwide acceptance. This method of fencing saves significant amounts of time, labor and materials, especially in rough country. Suspension fence cost about half as much as conventional fence. Functionally speaking, it is superior to traditional techniques due to its flexibility which makes it less apt to be broken by snowpack or tumbleweeds, and also accounts for the fact that it does less damage to the animal that runs into it than a more rigid fence. This concept typifies the Lasater Philosophy of Cattle Raising in that it resulted from the economic necessity of doing something better and cheaper than accepted methods permitted. It is one more example of a creative solution to the perennial problem of cost and function.

The construction of suspension fences involves good workmanship and materials, first and foremost. The success and durability of the installation, as well as its beauty, depends principally on two factors, good corners and a good stretch. Cattlemen have gone to great efforts to design corners or braces that can perform without being affected by soil temperature and moisture conditions. The only one that is truly foolproof is the "deadman," which consists of 4 wraps of double-strand barbed wire attached at ground level to an iron rod with an eye at the upper end which is set in cement at least three feet deep. Properly done, the "deadman" will not give and the fence will last the life of the material with little maintenance.

In open country, a stretch post should be placed each one-half mile. One roll of wire should be firmly attached with an electrician's splice to each stretch post and then stretched and spliced in the middle of the span where they meet. Stretching from the middle

PHOTO BY SALLY LASATER

A typical suspension gate installation showing the gate built of 2"x 4" rough lumber. In this case, the strap-iron diagonal on the gate is attached to the lowest bolt on the middle upright instead of the third bolt as recommended to prevent warping. This picture also illustrates one satisfactory way of constructing a corner that will not give. The posts and crossbars in this instance are of welded pipe. The twisted-wire diagonals on either side of the gate are attached to their respective "deadman," set in concrete under each end of the gate.

will give even tension on the whole span preventing sagging.

The Lasater Ranch presently installs a line post every 100 feet and a twisted steel wire stay every 20 feet on a five-wire fence. The stays should be twisted around the bottom wire to help keep them in place. At present, steel posts are used with corners made of railroad ties with a "deadman" on each side. The materials depend on availability and terrain. In many instances four or even three wires are adequate.

Where wooden posts are used, conventional staples are not adequate. The fence gripper, invented by my father in 1940, consists of a strip one-half inch by one and three-quarters inches of 18-gauge galvanized steel with a hole punched at each end. This strip is placed at a 45-degree angle over the wire and nailed with an 8-penny nail.

In extremely rocky terrain, holes can be drilled in the rock, and for posts, a piece of 1-inch angle-iron or other material driven into the holes which provides for inexpensive and very durable construction, utilizing the rock rather than combating it.

After the initial fence is built with 100-foot spans and one-half mile stretches, in some instances posts or "deadmen" must be added to pull the fence down in low areas or raise it where it touches the ground. However, in the case of a deep draw or arroyo a short fence or "watergap" should be constructed independent of the main one.

Suspension gates are invaluable in any area where it is feasible to use wooden gates. They are simple to construct, inexpensive, durable and attractive. Horizontally, the gates consist of four boards, 2"x4"x12' of rough lumber. Vertically, there are three boards, 2"x4"x4', one at each end and one in the middle of the gate. This lumber is bolted together with two washers between each two boards to prevent rotting. A piece of strap-iron with various holes drilled in each end to make it adjustable runs from the back or rear bolt on the gate hinge to the third or next-to-the-lowest bolt on the middle upright. Installed as shown on the opposite page, these gates will not sag.

"Down on the farm is different." †

CHAPTER XIV

TAXATION AND LAND OWNERSHIP

AMERICAN AGRICULTURAL PRODUCTIVITY is the marvel of the modern age. Malnutrition is still the world's number one problem. Since the beginning of time, man has tried to feed the world's people inadequately. By 2005, there will be six billion to feed. Russia and China are still struggling unsuccessfully to achieve self-sufficiency in their output of food and fiber.

In 1967, the average per capita intake per day in the underdeveloped countries was 2,000 calories. In the United States, it was 3,000 calories. However, this is only a quantitative comparison. In terms of quality, it required 400 pounds of grain to generate 2,000 calories per person per day in the underdeveloped world; whereas the 3,000-calory American intake required 1,600 pounds of grain per person per year.

In 1867, the American breadwinner spent 58% of his income on food. In 1967, the Russian breadwinner spent 53% of his income on food, while his American counterpart spent 18% on food.

The urban population, through its voting power, will decide the policies that determine how it will be fed and how the nation's land will be managed. There are two areas where the urban voting block should make enlightened decisions: (1) taxation and (2) policies affecting ownership of public and private lands. This chapter will outline a few of Tom Lasater's ideas on these matters.

From 1950-1967, United States farmland values rose 189%. Interest on farm debt increased 324%. Net farm income decreased 15%. In 1967, the age of the average farm owner was 58. These trends cannot continue.

Taxation should be limited to income taxes and sales taxes. After a person has earned money, he has the ability to pay as he does when he makes a purchase. Property taxes, such as those on land, are extremely unfair, for the property often does not have the earning capacity of a comparable investment in some urban business or in stocks and bonds. Land taxes, for the most part, are presently based on selling price rather than productivity.

In 1962, the New Jersey constitution was amended to provide that agricultural land be taxed on its productive capacity for agricultural purposes. The amendment also stipulated that land be held for at least two years to qualify for capital gains. The citizens of New Jersey were confronted with the possibility of taxing agriculture in "The Garden State" out of existence, and they intelligently chose to protect the legitimate agriculturalists, not only for their production but also to conserve some of the state's considerable rural beauty in the face of population growth and industrial expansion.

All policies affecting both public and private ownership of land should be based on the ancient biblical concept of stewardship, which says that the person privileged to own land is only the temporary custodian of it and is morally obligated to leave that land in better condition than he found it. It would be impossible for a true cattleman to view the situation differently. The historic custom existed in some parts of Europe never to remove a tree without planting one to take its place.

The basis of Tom Lasater's philosophy is the realization that good genetics, good conservation and good economics are completely compatible. This innate belief in the balance of nature, of which man is a part, should govern all land ownership policies, for we are no longer in a situation where we have frontier land waiting to replace areas damaged or ruined by abuse. Our laws should be such that a selfish individual or company will not be allowed to plunder nature.

Vine Deloria, Jr., in his new book, has the following to say about the Lasater Ranch:

> The concept is not impossible. Already a rancher in Colorado has tried the idea of grazing wild animals and beef cattle on his range with excellent results. Tom Lasater has a 26,000-acre ranch east of Colorado Springs, Colorado. He has pursued a no-shooting, no-poisoning, no-killing program for his land. There has already been a substantial increase

in game animals, primarily mule deer and antelope, without any disturbance to his beef animals. Lasater first decided to allow wild animals to remain on his land when his foreman remarked, after the prairie dogs had been exterminated, that the grass always grew better when the prairie dogs had been allowed to live on the land.

The result of Lasater's allowing the land to return to its primitive state has been the notable decrease of weeds. Lasater feels that the smaller animals, such as gophers, ground squirrels, badgers and prairie dogs, that dig holes all provided a better means of aerating the ground and introducing more oxygen into it than modern farming methods of periodically turning the soil by plowing. All of the wildlife use on the land produced better grazing land and reduced the danger of overgrazing in a remarkable way. The fantastic thing about Lasater's ranch is that it returns almost double the income from beef cattle, because of the improved conditions of the soil and the better grasses, than would the average ranch of comparable acreage using the so-called modern techniques of ranching.

The genius of returning the land to its original animals is that the whole program cuts down on labor costs, maintains fertility far better than modern techniques, increases environmental stability, and protects the soil from water and wind erosion. The net result is that the land supports much more life, wild and domestic, and is in better shape to continue to support life once the program is underway. . . .[11]

These are policies that should be followed on both public and private lands. Landowners should take the initiative in restoring our rangelands to their wilderness state. They should be compensated for the beauty of their land as well as for the game it supports. It would be preferable for land that is now privately owned to continue to be privately owned, for parks pay no taxes and produce very little, while farms and ranches pay taxes and produce much.

If today's landowners do not rise to this challenge, then increasing public ownership is inevitable, just as the government has now entered the pollution issue because of the failure of private enterprise to act in time.

The public lands presently in existence need to be managed with overall ecological considerations in mind. At the moment, agriculture, mining, tourism and other groups are being allowed to abuse some of the nation's land for their own short-term gain. No poisoning or trapping of predators with a view to their elimination should be permitted nor should any activities that contribute to any pollution or defacement of our rural areas be tolerated. Tourism, as it exists today in our national parks, is nothing more than a form of pollution – and one of the worst we have.

Both the urban voting block and the agricultural segment of the economy should each act and vote with its long-range interest in mind – from a vantage-point of "intelligent selfishness" – to use one of Tom Lasater's phrases.

PHOTO BY DAROL DICKINSON

"Old bull for pedigree – young bull for insurance." †

CHAPTER XV

THE ORIGIN OF THE BEEFMASTER BREED

When Tom Lasater entered the cattle business in 1931, it was not with the idea of forming a new breed of cattle but to produce "more beef for less money," to quote a slogan coined by F. R. Carpenter. In the process of experimenting with various combinations of the three breeds at hand (Hereford, Shorthorn, Brahman) he quickly discovered that the three-way cross was superior to any other combination and converted his entire herd to that cross. Beefmasters were recognized as a breed by the United States Department of Agriculture in 1954.

Ed C. Lasater (Tom Lasater's father) was an extremely far-sighted cattleman and had introduced the Brahman cattle to South Texas in 1908. He had also developed a superior herd of Hereford cattle that were heavy milkers and had red circles around the eyes, which made them resistant to eye troubles.

The following on the origin of the Beefmaster breed is quoted from U.S.D.A. Farmer's Bulletin No. 2228:

> The development of the breed was begun in 1931 by Tom Lasater on a ranch near Falfurrias, Texas. The foundation herd of the breed was moved in 1949 to Matheson, Colorado, where development continues.
>
> Three breeds – the Hereford, the Shorthorn, and the Brahman – were combined to produce the Beefmaster. In the initial crosses, Mr. Lasater used both the registered Hereford and the Brahman herd, which had been developed by his father, Edward C. Lasater, who began his work with Brahman cattle in 1908. The foundation herd was closed since the purchase of a few registered Shorthorn sires during the 1930's.
>
> The majority of the crossbreeding was carried on in multiple-sire herds under range conditions; hence, the exact percentage of blood of each of the parent breeds is not known. It is estimated that about 25 percent Hereford, 25 percent Shorthorn and 50 percent Brahman hereditary material was incorporated into the breed.

"Bulls should look like bulls."†

During the entire period of breed development, selection has been practiced for disposition, fertility, weight, conformation, hardiness, and milk production. No planned selection for coat color has ever been made. However, there has been an apparent increase in the frequency of red.[12]

Only cattle that are purebred descendants of the foundation herd (Lasater Beefmasters) or are produced by three consecutive top-crosses of recognized breeding may be called Beefmasters. No distinction is made between artificial insemination and natural service.

In order that each animal may be permanently identified with the breeder, the use of a prefix name such as Lasater Beefmasters, Casey Beefmasters or Coahuila Beefmasters is obligatory. Thus, responsibility is placed squarely upon the shoulders of the individual breeder.

Beefmasters are the only recognized breed of cattle in existence that have been selected solely for beef-making characteristics from the beginning.

"The pedigree is in the name."— MARY CASEY LASATER

"The breeding and management program which we follow has often been described as survival of the fittest where we define fit." †

CHAPTER XVI

CONCLUSION

IN THE FOREGOING PAGES, the author has briefly outlined the Lasater Philosophy of Cattle Raising – the only existing proven ranch management system that encompasses all aspects of the business from range ecology through merchandising. Tom Lasater's outlook has been described as creative radicalism whereby he advocates abandonment of many traditional management and selling practices, but always suggests a specific alternative. The reader can supply the specific information necessary to adapt this philosophy to his particular environment, wherever that may be.

The SIX ESSENTIALS and the Lasater concept of reproductive efficiency have been discussed in detail. These principles are very simple but their execution requires a great deal of integrity and will power due to the extreme criteria applied in each instance. Tom Lasater's thoughts in regard to breed associations summarize this idea of individual effort and responsibility: "When all the rules and regulations governing the breeding of cattle are boiled down, it is the integrity of the breeder, and only his integrity, which determines the outcome. No breed association in the world could possibly know which bull sired which calf out of which cow. Only the man in charge of his cattle knows."

It has been shown that a partnership with nature is one of the keystones of the Lasater method. The idea of slaughtering a cow whose calf is killed by a bear or coyote rather than killing the bear or coyote has been unique in the industry for many years. The same concept is being applied to parasites – the animal unduly affected is culled. It has now become apparent in all phases of life and agriculture that our society should return to the concept of the balance of nature, of which man is a part. There exists, on the Lasater Ranch, living proof of the long term economic and environmental benefits of an intimate partnership with nature.

Tom Lasater has a great love for the people and history of the cattle business and is always pleased to have his ideas presented. Writing this book has been of great help to its author in forcing him to think through many things previously not fully understood. It is certain that my father will be pleased if the reader is likewise stimulated to understand more fully the challenges facing the industry as a whole as well as how to increase the satisfaction in and profitability of his own operation.

PHOTO BY STEWARTS

"Better beef begins with BEEFMASTERS."— MARY CASEY LASATER

Appendix A

The Case for the Cattle Producer

(From a speech by Mr. F. R. Carpenter at a convention of Better Beef, Inc.)

A new product called "Fed Beef" is the cause of the revolution which has been going on in the beef industry for the past twenty years.

The multiplication of the big year-round commercial feedlots; the relocation of packing plants to be nearer sources of supply; the chaining up of self-service, self-delivery retail meat stores, and last but not least, the modernized animal husbandry of cattle producers, are all attributable to the shift in consumer preference, from "grass" to "fed" beef.

The pay-off has been an increase in per capita consumption of beef from 59 lbs. in 1950 to 114 lbs. in 1970. Seventy-five percent of the increase being in "Fed Beef."

In sharing the prosperity of this expansion, the cattle producer is "the forgotten man." The price of his cattle has remained constant while his expenses have increased 113%.

If this oddity was the result of sloth or inefficiency, it would be understandable. All signs point in another direction. Cattle growers have increased the average cow production by 35% in this period. Increased efficiency in cattle production exceeds that of any other segment of the beef industry.

The real cause of frozen cattle prices is directly traceable to antiquated marketing practices by packers. They have clung to standards of value applicable to grass-fed cattle but entirely unrealistic when used for fed cattle. The retailers have acquiesced in this fiction.

The hanging beef carcass has always been the standard of value of cattle for slaughter. For grass-fed cattle it was "the trunk of an animal after the hide, head, limbs, edible organs and offal have been removed; the dressed body."

Fed beef carcasses, however, in addition to the by-products of grass beef carcasses, have another by-product not found in the latter. It is excess fat which consumers refuse to buy on beef cuts. On a 600-lb. fed beef carcass, choice grade, this will average 125 to 150 lbs. or one-fourth of the entire weight of the carcass. This by-product, excess fat, is only worth one-tenth of what the rest of the carcass is worth, but it is sold at the same price. This throws the old definition of a beef carcass out of reality as a standard of value for fed cattle.

The continued use of this false standard has not only frozen cattle prices, it has been used as an excuse for paying less for high cutting cattle than for low cutting ones of the same grade.

'Til this fiction is abolished and a new fair standard of value for cattle be accepted, the present trend to make cattle production an adjunct of the feeder, processor or distributor segments will continue.

The whole situation was well summed up in the U. S. Department of Agriculture Report No. 95, entitled "Agricultural Markets in Change." It says: A major portion of slaughter livestock sold in this country last year — perhaps more than 95% — were sold in about the same way that livestock were sold in Biblical times. The Buyer and Seller haggled over the quality and yield of the livestock. Finally came to an agreement and a deal was made. That this system is obsolete, and that it will give way to something more efficient is no longer a question — *eventually the present system for selling livestock for slaughter will be completely reorganized.* Slaughter cattle will very likely be sold on the basis of price per pound of dressed carcass. The price will depend on both the quality and the quantity of the lean meat produced. Those facts will be determined by an objective Grader, who will use the Federal Grading System or some variant of it.

As to whom will demand the change, G. Alvin Carpenter, Agricultural Economist for the University of California at Berkeley, puts it squarely when he says:

The road to improved bargaining power for Livestock Producers may be difficult, but no matter, if improvement is to be made, producers themselves will have to work together effectively with other segments of the industry to do it. No one else will.

Better Beef, Inc., is the only organization I know dedicated to reforming this market monstrosity.

To promote a product, however, it must first be identified.

This has been the effort of Better Beef, Inc., for the past two years. This meeting will judge its efforts and determine its future course.

Appendix B

The Lasater Beefmaster Standard of Excellence

THE LASATER BEEFMASTER STANDARD OF EXCELLENCE is exemplified by the animal which embodies, to a marked degree, all of the Six Essential Beefmaster Characteristics: Disposition, Fertility, Weight, Conformation, Hardiness, and Milk Production. The Lasater Ranch demands and develops these Six Essentials in the following ways:

1. DISPOSITION.

Having been raised under identical range conditions, the difference in disposition between individuals is readily apparent during the first several days following weaning. Those with poor dispositions are culled. Thereafter, disposition is judged continually.

2. FERTILITY.

(a) Males: Our bulls go into service at 12½ to 14½ months of age. As all breeding is carried on in large, multi-sire herds, the bulls most capable of actually settling cows under range conditions leave the most inheritance in the herd. Those least capable leave the least; the infertile leave no progeny.

(b) Females: Our heifers are first bred at 12½ to 14½ months of age. All age groups are bred under range conditions with no hay during a short, 65-day winter breeding season, beginning on November 15th. Each female must conceive during this short breeding season and then wean a good calf — no exceptions — or be culled.

3. WEIGHT.

(a) Males: Selection for weight among our herd sires is based primarily upon weaning weight and post-weaning gain. The weaning weight reflects the milking ability of the dam. The post-weaning gain indicates the efficiency of the individual's own "carburetor."

(b) Females: At weaning time light-weight heifer calves are culled. Thereafter, a cow is not culled on her own weight but for weaning a light-weight calf.

4. CONFORMATION.

Conformation is judged as it relates to "type on the hook," not "type on the hoof." The ideal conformation is exemplified by that animal whose carcass will yield the most pounds of tender, lean beef per pound of live weight.

5. Hardiness.

Hardiness is exemplified by those animals which carry on their relentless production assignment year after year with minimum assistance.

6. Milk production.

(a) Males: As only bull calves with *top weaning weights* are considered as potential herd sires, they perpetuate the heavy milking qualities of their dams.

(b) Females: Light-weight calves from poor milking dams are culled at weaning. Cows weaning light-weight calves are culled.

The Lasater Beefmaster Standard of Excellence is the *only beef cattle selection standard in the world* which concerns itself solely with the Six Essential Characteristics required to produce beef efficiently.

PHOTO BY STEWARTS

"Cows should look like cows." †

"Cattle breeding is a relatively simple endeavor. The only difficult part is to keep it simple." †

REFERENCES

1. *Western Livestock Journal,* September 1970, p. 21.
2. Rangeman's News, June, 1970.
3. Peter F. Drucker, *Managing for Results,* (New York, 1964), p. 5.
4. *Rangeman's News,* June, 1970.
5. Dr. D. R. Mackey, "How to Prevent Dark Cutters," *Feedlot,* April, 1971, p. 70.
6. Dr. T. C. Cartwright, "Longevity: A Valuable Fertility Trait," *The Cattleman,* February, 1971, p. 43.
7. *The West Texas Livestock Weekly,* Dec. 8, 1970, p. 3.
8. John C. Pierce, "A New Dimension in Beef Grading," *Agricultural Marketing,* July, 1965.
9. An opinion expressed in conversation by Dr. M. E. Ensminger.
10. U.S.D.A. Report No. 95, "Agricultural Markets in Change."
11. Vine Deloria, Jr., *We Talk, You Listen,* (New York, 1970), p. 191.
12. U.S.D.A. *Farmer's Bulletin* No. 2228, pp. 17-18.

"The only thing a bull needs a head for is to take in groceries and emit a mating call." †

Acknowledgements

Many persons have contributed to the completion of this book, and to each of them I wish to express my gratitude.

First and foremost, thanks are due my wife, Annette, for her typing and proofreading. I am also grateful to her for supporting my efforts to become established in the cattle business.

Mr. and Mrs. Tom Lasater of Matheson, Colorado, have made available to me the pictures used and given me free access to their files. The project could not have been undertaken without their full cooperation.

Three additional persons have contributed ideas or information that added greatly to the value of the book. They are: F. R. Carpenter of Hayden, Colorado; Dougles D. Christopher of San Jose, Costa Rica; and Duke Phillips of Sabinas, Coahuila, Mexico.

Those who read the manuscript from a critical standpoint, and thereby were of great assistance include: Sally Lasater, Dale Lasater, and Stephen Parrinder of London, England.

I am also grateful to Ben E. Pingenot and Harper Sparks, both of Eagle Pass, Texas, for the valuable information they freely gave me in regard to publication of the book, and to Haywood Antone for editorial assistance, and to Carl Hertzog for design and typography, both of El Paso, Texas.

Finally, I wish to thank the MacMillan Co., for permission to quote from Vine Deloria, Jr.'s *We Talk, You Listen,* and to Harper & Row Publishers for permission to quote from *Managing for Results* by Peter F. Drucker.